It's Easy To Play
Boyzone.

Wise Publications
London / New York / Paris / Sydney / Copenhagen / Madrid / Tokyo

Exclusive Distributors:

Music Sales Limited
8/9 Frith Street, London W1V 5TZ, England.

Music Sales Pty Limited
120 Rothschild Avenue, Rosebery, NSW 2018, Australia.

Order No. AM966515
ISBN 0-7119-8400-X
This book © Copyright 2000 by Wise Publications.

Cover photograph courtesy of All Action
Compiled by Nick Crispin.
Music arranged by Stephen Duro.
Music processed by Allegro Reproductions.

Music Sales' complete catalogue describes thousands of titles and
is available in full colour sections by subject, direct from Music Sales Limited.
Please state your areas of interest and send a cheque/postal order for £1.50 for postage to:
Music Sales Limited, Newmarket Road, Bury St. Edmunds, Suffolk IP33 3YB.

www.musicsales.com

Your Guarantee of Quality:
As publishers, we strive to produce every book to the highest commercial standards.
The music has been freshly engraved and the book has been carefully designed to minimise awkward page turns and to make playing from it a real pleasure.
Particular care has been given to specifying acid-free, neutral-sized paper made from pulps which have not been elemental chlorine bleached.
This pulp is from farmed sustainable forests and was produced with special regard for the environment.
Throughout, the printing and binding have been planned to ensure a sturdy, attractive publication which should give years of enjoyment.
If your copy fails to meet our high standards, please inform us and we will gladly replace it.

Printed in the United Kingdom by
Caligraving Limited, Thetford, Norfolk.

A Different Beat

Words & Music by Martin Brannigan, Stephen Gately, Ronan Keating,
Shane Lynch, Ray Hedges & Keith Duffy

Moderately

Verse 2:

Humanity has lost face,
Let's understand its grace,
Each day, one at a time,
Each life, including mine.

Let's take a stand and look around us now,
People,
So let's take a stand and look around us now'
People, oh people, oh people.

All That I Need

Words & Music by Evan Rogers & Carl Sturken

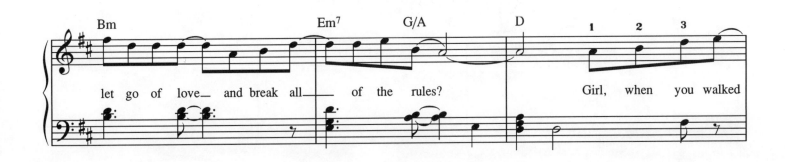

let go of love___ and break all___ of the rules?   Girl, when you walked

___ out that door, left a hole___ in my heart and now I___ know for sure;___

___ You're the air that I breathe___ girl, you're all that I need.___

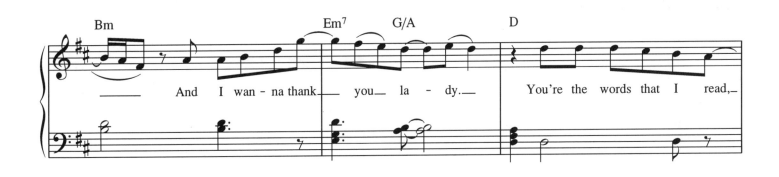

___ And I wan - na thank___ you___ la - dy.___   You're the words that I read,___

___ you're the light that I see,___   and your love is all___ that I need.___

You're the song that I sing,— girl, you're my ev-'ry-thing.— And I wan-na thank—

— you— la - dy.— You're all that I need-ed girl, You're the air that I breathe, yeah.

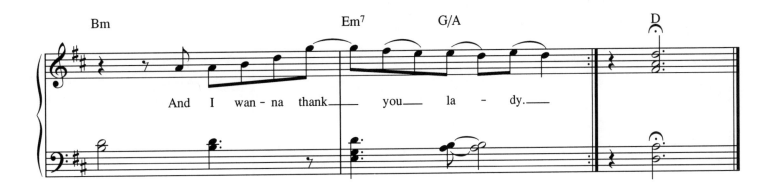

And I wan - na thank— you— la - dy.—

Verse 2:

I was searching in vain, playing your game
Had no-one else but myself left to blame
You came into my world, no diamonds or pearls
Could ever replace what you gave to me girl
Just like a castle of sand
Girl I almost let love
Slip right out of my hand
And just like the flower needs rain
I will stand by your side
Through the joy and the pain.

You're the air that I breathe *etc.*

Baby Can I Hold You

Words & Music by Tracy Chapman

(Ba - by if I told you._)   (Ba - by,_)You'd be mine.

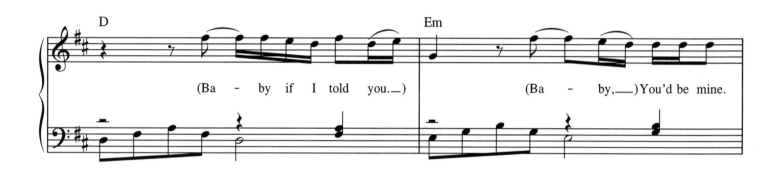

(Ba - by if I told you._)   (Ba - by,_)You'd be mine.

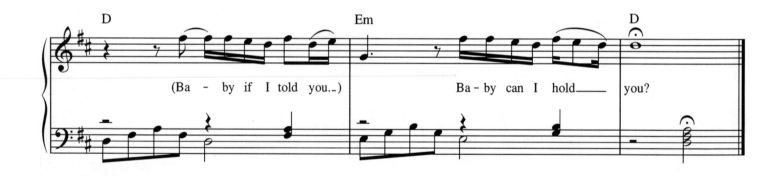

(Ba - by if I told you..)   Ba - by can I hold___ you?

Verse 2:

Forgive me is all that you can't say
Years gone by and still
Words don't come easily
Like forgive me, forgive me.

Verse 3:

I love you is all that you can't say
Years gone by and still
Words don't come easily
Like I love you, I love you.

Every Day I Love You

Words & Music by Frank J. Myers, Gary Baker & Jerry Williams

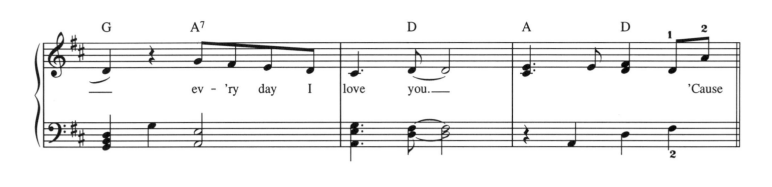

ev - 'ry day I love you.___ 'Cause

I be - lieve___ that des - ti - ny___ is out___ of our___ con -

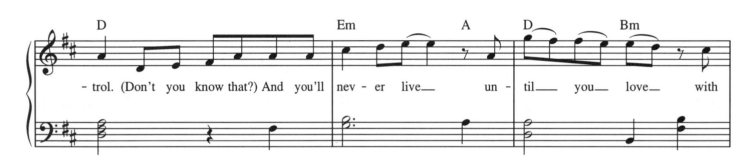

- trol. (Don't you know that?) And you'll nev - er live___ un - til___ you___ love___ with

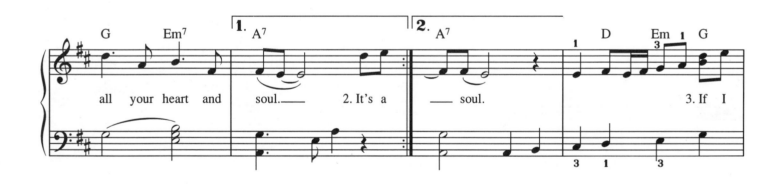

all your heart and soul.___ 2. It's a ___ soul. 3. If I

asked would you___ say yes?___ To - geth - er we're the ve - ry best,___ I know that

I am tru – ly blessed___ ev-'ry day I love you.___ Ooh._____ And

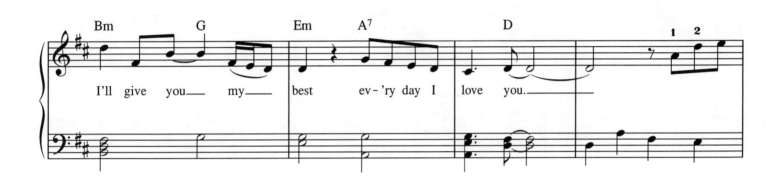

I'll give you___ my___ best ev-'ry day I love you.___

Oh yeah._

Verse 2:
It's a touch when I feel bad
It's a smile when I get mad
All the little things I have
Everyday I love you.
Instrumental break.

'Cause I believe *etc.*

Father And Son

Words & Music by Cat Stevens

Moderately

1. It's not time to make a change; just re - lax, take it ea - sy. You're still
(Verse 2 see block lyric)

young, that's your fault; there's so much you have to know.__ Find a girl,__

__ set - tle down; if you want,__ you can mar - ry. Look at

me: I am old but I'm hap - py. 2. I was still be here to - mor-row, but your dreams may

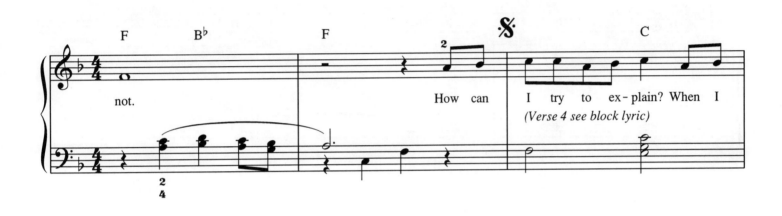

not. How can I try to ex - plain? When I
(Verse 4 see block lyric)

do he turns a - way a - gain. Well, it's al - ways been the same, same old

sto - ry.___ From the mo - ment I could talk, I was or - dered to list - en;___ now there's a

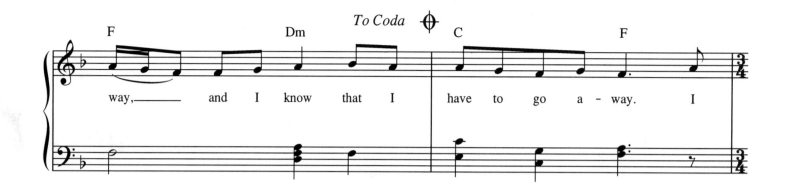

way,_____ and I know that I have to go a - way. I

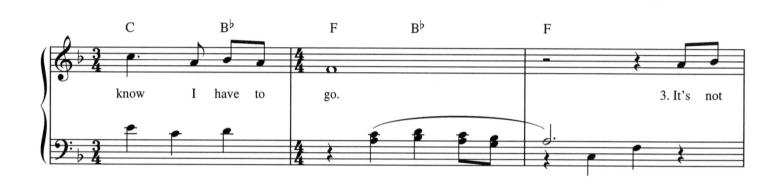

know I have to go. 3. It's not

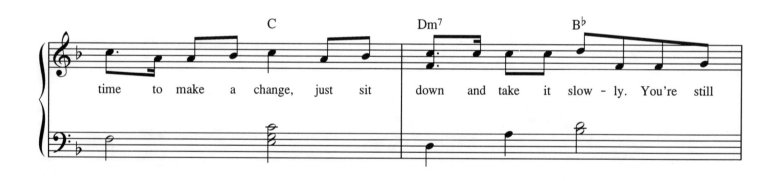

time to make a change, just sit down and take it slow - ly. You're still

young, that's your fault; there's so much you have to go through. Find a

girl, set – tle down; if you want, you can mar – ry. Look at

D.S. al Coda

me: I am old but I'm hap – py. 4. All the

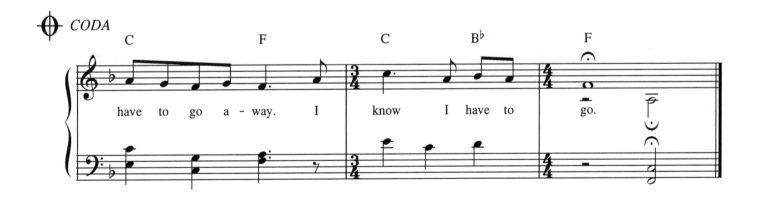

CODA

have to go a – way. I know I have to go.

Verse 2:

I was once like you are now;
And I know that it's not easy
To be calm when you've found something going on.
But take your time, think a lot;
Think of everything you've got.
For you will still be here tomorrow,
But your dreams may not.

Verse 4:

All the times that I've cried,
Keeping all the things I knew inside;
And it's hard, but it's harder to ignore it.
If they were right I'd agree,
But it's them they know, not me;
Now there's a way, and I know
That I have to go away.
I know I have to go.

I Love The Way You Love Me

Words & Music by Chuck Cannon & Victoria Shaw

Moderately

1. I like the feel of your name on my lips and I like the sound of your sweet

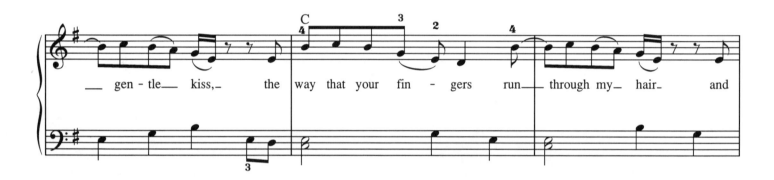

gen - tle kiss, the way that your fin - gers run through my hair and

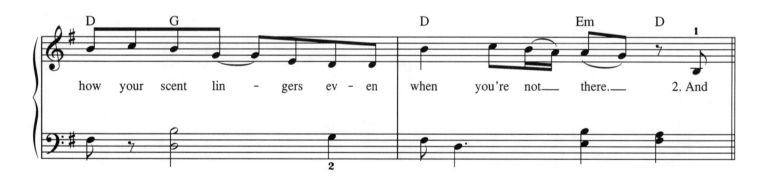

how your scent lin - gers ev - en when you're not there. 2. And

I like the way your eyes dance when you laugh and how you'll en - joy your two

(Verse 3 see block lyric)

To Coda

so com-plete-ly. I____ love the way____ you love____

____ me,____ yeah.____ (So list-en to me now) And ____ me.

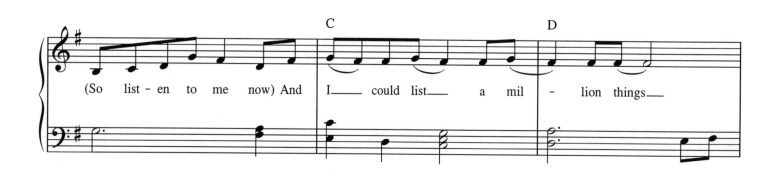

(So list-en to me now) And I____ could list____ a mil - lion things____

I'd love to like a - bout____ you. (A - bout____ you) But they all come____ down to____

24

one— rea - son,   I could ne - ver live— with - out— you. I

CODA

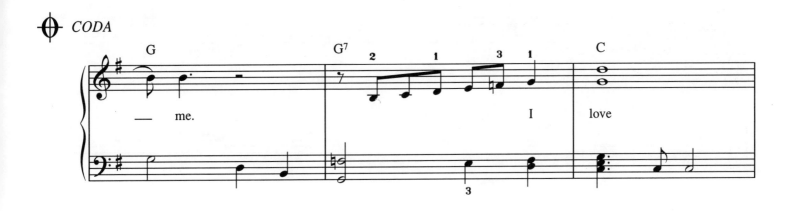

— me.   I love

the way— that you love— me.

Verse 3:

And I like the sound of old R and B
You roll your eyes when I'm slightly off key
And I like the innocent way that you cry
From sappy old movies you've seen thousands of times.

But I love *etc.*

Love Me For A Reason

Words & Music by Johnny Bristol, Wade Brown, Jr. & David Jones

Moderately

1. Girl, when you hold___ me, how you con-trol___ me; you
(Verse 2 see block lyric)

bend and you fold___ me a-ny-way you please.

It must be ea-sy for___ you, the love-ly things that you___ do are

just a pas-time for___ you, I could ne-ver be.

D.S. al Coda

CODA

love me for a rea - son, let the rea - son be love. Don't love me for fun, girl,

let me be— the one, girl, love me for a rea - son, let the rea - son be love.

Verse 2:

Kisses and caresses are only minor tests, babe,
Of love needs and stresses between a woman and a man.
So if love everlasting isn't what you're asking,
I'll have to pass, girl; I'm proud to take a stand.
I can't continue guessing, because it's only messing
With my pride and my mind.
So write down this time to time:

To Chorus

D.S.:

I'm just a little old-fashioned,
It takes more than a physical attraction.
My initial reaction is "Honey, give me love;
Not a facsimile of."

To Chorus

Picture Of You

Words & Music by Eliot Kennedy, Ronan Keating, Paul Wilson & Andy Watkins

—— it could be—— so wrong,—— Why'd it take—— me so long—— just to find

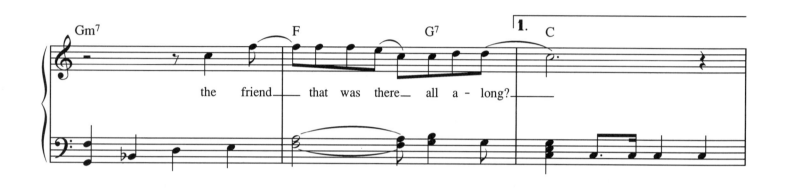

the friend—— that was there—— all a - long?

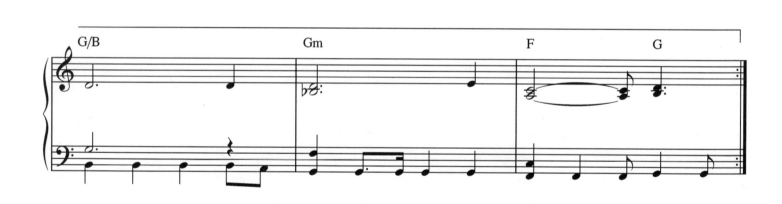

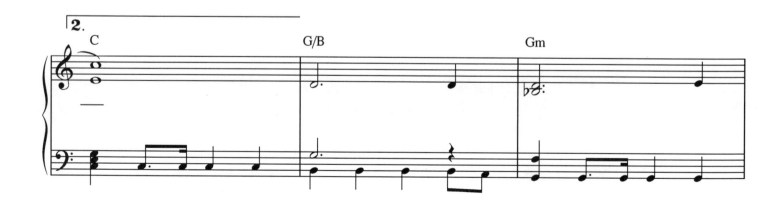

You were with me there___ when I need - ed some - bo - dy.___

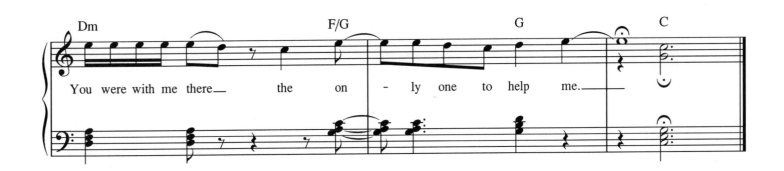

You were with me there___ the on - ly one to help me.___

Verse 3:

Did you believe that after all that we've been through
I'd be able to put my trust in you?
Goes to show you can forgive and forget
Looking back I have no regrets, 'cos

You were with me there *etc.*

No Matter What

Music by Andrew Lloyd Webber
Lyrics by Jim Steinman

Remember.
Bb + Eb
Bb major

Moderately

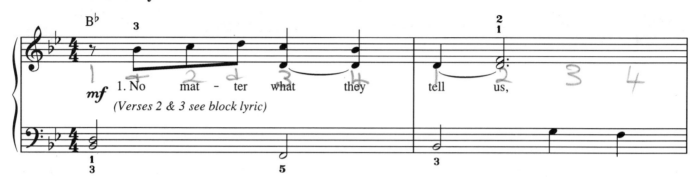

mf 1. No mat-ter what they tell us,

(Verses 2 & 3 see block lyric)

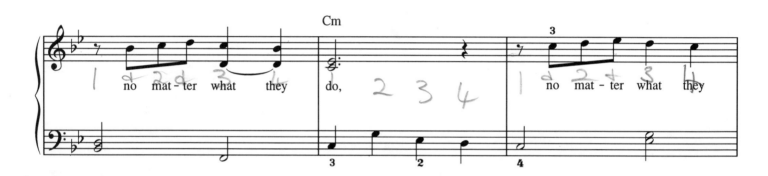

no mat-ter what they do, no mat-ter what they

teach us, what we be-lieve is true.

No mat-ter what they call us, how-ev-er they at-

- tack, no mat - ter where they take us,

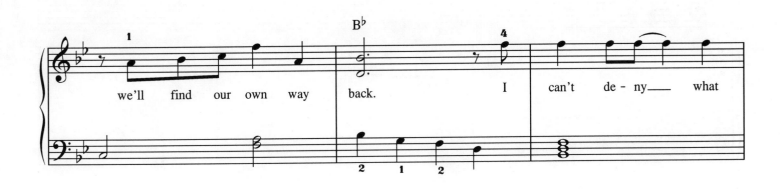

we'll find our own way back. I can't de - ny___ what

I be - lieve,___ I can't be___ what I'm not.___

1, 2.

I know our love's for - ev - er, I know no mat - ter

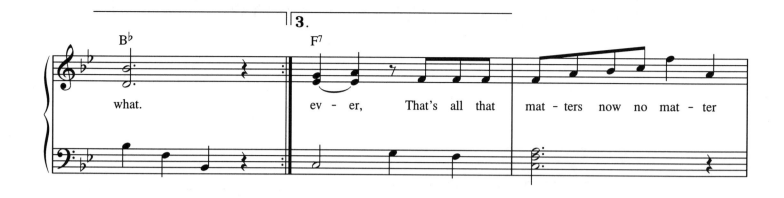

what.   ev - er,   That's all that   mat - ters now no mat - ter

what.   I know no mat - ter   what.

Verse 2:

If only tears were laughter,
If only night was day,
If only prayers were answered
Then we would hear God say.
No matter what they tell us,
No matter what they do,
No matter what they teach you,
What you believe is true.
And I will keep you safe and strong
And sheltered from the storm.
No matter where it's barren
Our dream is being born.

Verse 3:
Instrumental:

No matter if the sun don't shine,
Or if the skies are blue.
No matter what the ending,
My life began with you.
I can't deny what I believe,
I can't be what I'm not.
I know this love's for ever,
That's all that matters now no matter what.

When You Say Nothing At All

Words & Music by Paul Overstreet & Don Schlitz

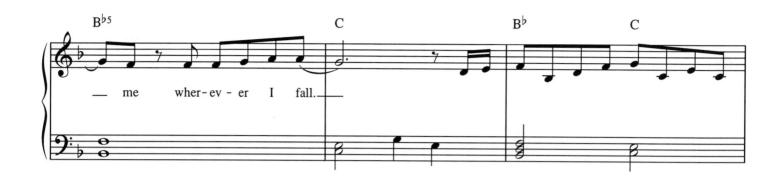

me   wher- ev - er   I   fall.

You   say   it   best   when you   say   no - thing   at   all.

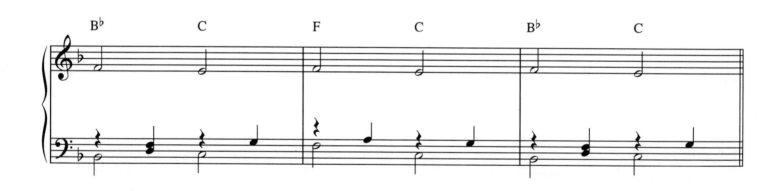

(You   say   it   best   when   you   say   no - thing   at   all.   )

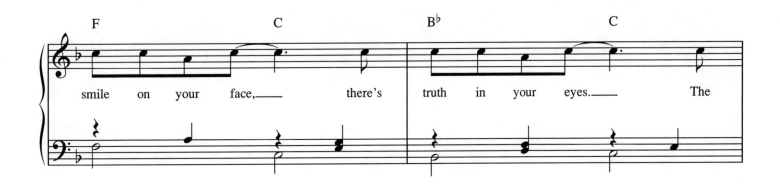

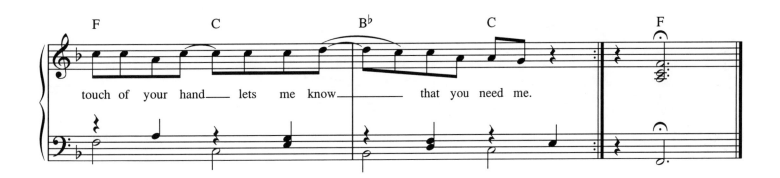

Verse 2:

All day long I can hear people talking out loud
But when you hold me you drown out the crowd
Try as they may they can never defy
What's been said between your heart and mine.

The smile on your face *etc.*

You Needed Me

Words & Music by Randy Goodrum

can't be-lieve it's you,___ I can't___ be - lieve it's true._____ I

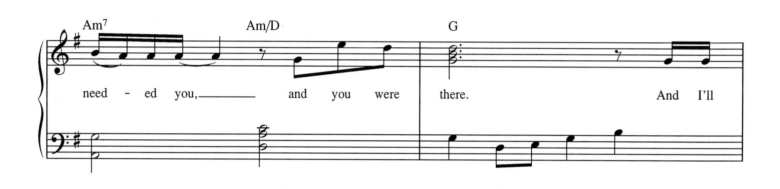

need - ed you,_____ and you were there. And I'll

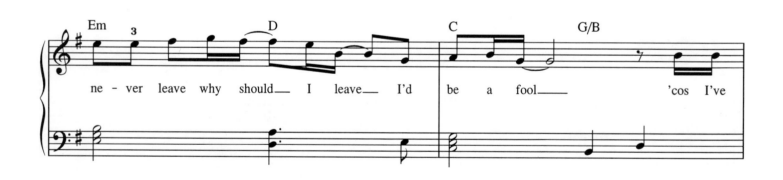

ne - ver leave why should___ I leave___ I'd be a fool____ 'cos I've

D.S. al Coda

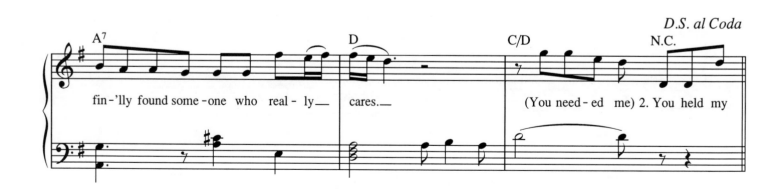

fin-'lly found some-one who real - ly___ cares.___ (You need - ed me) 2. You held my

need - ed me.____ You need - ed me.____ You

need - ed me.____ Oh yes you need - ed me.____ You

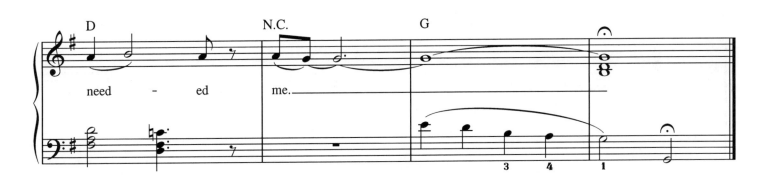

need - ed me.____

Verse 2:

You held my hand
When it was cold
When I was lost
You took me home
You gave me hope
When I was at the end
And turned my lies
Back into truth again
You even called me friend.

You gave me strength
To stand alone again *etc.*

For Jan 15th

 # Words

Words & Music by Barry Gibb, Robin Gibb & Maurice Gibb

Moderato   R. Hand   to   ✷

Moderately

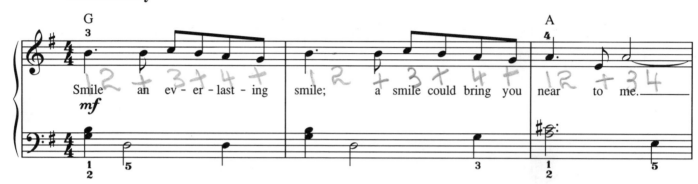

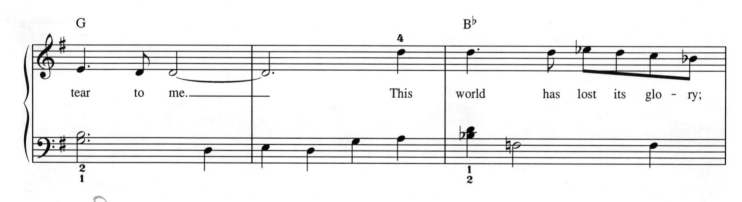

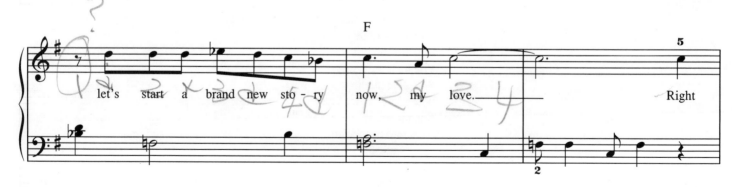

46

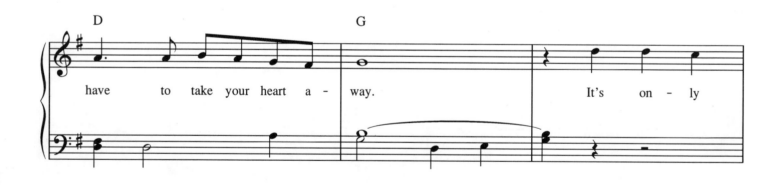